Specimen Sight-Reading Tests for Trombone 𝄞 and 𝄢 and Bass Trombone

Grades 6–8

ABRSM

Printed in England by Caligraving Ltd, Thetford, Norfolk,
on materials from sustainable sources
Reprinted in 2018

GRADE 6

© 1998 by The Associated Board of the Royal Schools of Music

Trombone 𝄞

GRADE 7

Trombone 𝄢

AB 2690